For Jason, my forever friend
~CF
For Anna, with all my love
~BC

Text Copyright © 2007 by Claire Freedman
Illustration Copyright © 2007 by Ben Cort
Published by arrangement with Simon & Schuster UK Ltd
1st Floor, 222 Gray's Inn Road, London, WC1X 8HB
A CBS Company

Dual language text copyright © 2011 Mantra Lingua
Audio copyright © 2011 Mantra Lingua
A CIP record for this book is available from the British Library
Mantra Lingua, Global House, 303 Ballards Lane, London, N12 8NP

www.mantralingua.com

Printed in Hatfield, UK FP300612PB08127190

Hear each page of this talking book narrated in many languages
with TalkingPEN! Then record your own versions.

Touch the arrow below with the TalkingPEN to start

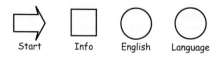

Start   Info   English   Language

A los Marcianos les Encantan los Calzoncillos
Aliens Love Underpants

Claire Freedman & Ben Cort

Spanish translation by Marta Belen Saez-Cabero

Mantra Lingua

A los marcianos les encantan los calzoncillos,
De todas formas y tipos.
Pero no hay calzoncillos en el espacio,
Y esto te cortará el hipo…

Aliens love underpants,
Of every shape and size.
But there are no underpants in space,
So here's a big surprise…

Cuando los marcianos bajan a la Tierra,
No vienen a por TI...
Simplemente quieren tus calzoncillos –
¡Te aseguro que sí!

When aliens fly down to Earth, they don't come to meet YOU...
They simply want your underpants - I'll bet you never knew!

El radar de su nave pita y parpadea al encontrar
Calzoncillos en una cuerda que se mueven sin parar.

Their spaceship's radar bleeps and blinks the moment that it sees
A washing line of underpants all flapping in the breeze.

Aterrizan en tu jardín, sin invitación.
"¡Mira, CALZONCILLOS!" gritan,
Y bailan llenos de emoción.

They land in your back garden, though they haven't been invited.
"Oooooh, UNDERPANTS!" they chant, and dance around, delighted.

Les gustan naranjas como mandarinas,
Les gustan verdes, les gustan rojos.
Pero los bombachos con lunares de la Abuela
Hacen que se les salgan los ojos.

They like them red, they like them green, or orange like satsumas.
But best of all they love the sight of Granny's spotted bloomers.

Juegan al escondite en las bragas rosas con volantes de Mamá
Y los calzoncillos largos de lana del Abuelo son un gran tobogán.

Mum's pink frilly knickers are a perfect place to hide
And Grandpa's woolly longjohns make a super-whizzy slide.

In daring competitions, held up by just one peg,
They count how many aliens can squeeze inside each leg.

Se cuelgan de una pinza
Demostrando gran valor,
Y cuentan cuántos marcianos
Caben en su interior.

Llevan calzoncillos en los pies,
En la cabeza y en otros curiosos lugares.
¡Hacen carreras haciendo el pino y los cuelgan de sus naves!

They wear pants on their feet and heads and other silly places.
They fly pants from their spaceships and hold Upside-Down-Pant Races!

Usan el elástico para rebotar y zumbar.
¡Es c-alucinante ver a los marcianos jugar!

As they go zinging through the air,
it really is pants-tastic.
What fun the aliens can have
with pingy pants elastic!

No culpes al perro del vecino
O a la gente que vive al lado.
Cuando los calzoncillos desaparezcan,
¡Échale la culpa a los MARCIANOS!

It's not your neighbour's naughty dog, or next-door's funny game.
When underpants go missing, the ALIENS are to blame!

But quick! Mum's coming out to fetch the washing in at last.
Wheee! Off the aliens all zoom, they're used to leaving fast…

¡Cuidado, marcianos!
Mamá viene a por la colada.
¡Zum! Todos desaparecen
Como si aquí no hubiera pasado nada.

¡Así que mira en tus calzoncillos bien planchados y frescos,
Por si acaso un marciano se ha quedado atascado adentro!

So when you put your pants on, freshly washed and nice and clean,
Just check in case an alien still lurks inside, unseen!